DISNEY
✦ PRINCESS

JASMINE

A Story of Honesty

Adapted by Lisa Harkrader
Illustrated by the Disney Storybook Artists

Published by Louis Weber, C.E.O., Publications International, Ltd.
7373 North Cicero Avenue, Lincolnwood, Illinois 60712

Ground Floor, 59 Gloucester Place, London W1U 8JJ

Customer Service: 1-800-595-8484 or customer_service@pilbooks.com

www.pilbooks.com

p i kids is a registered trademark of Publications International, Ltd.

Manufactured in China.

8 7 6 5 4 3 2 1

ISBN-13: 978-1-4127-6777-4

ISBN-10: 1-4127-6777-6

publications international, ltd.

A long time ago, there was a young man named Aladdin who lived on the streets of Agrabah. Although Aladdin was very poor, he had dreams of becoming rich.

"Can you imagine what it would be like to live at the Sultan's palace?" asked Aladdin.

Abu, Aladdin's pet monkey, snored in response.

"Well, I think it would be wonderful," sighed Aladdin, as he drifted off to sleep.

At that very moment, the Sultan's daughter was thinking that the palace wasn't very wonderful at all. Princess Jasmine was supposed to marry before her next birthday. Princes had come from faraway kingdoms to try to win her heart, but Jasmine didn't want to marry them. She told her father that she had to be true to herself. She couldn't live a lie.

Sneaking quietly past the guards, Princess Jasmine ran away from her palace home!

The next morning, a disguised Princess Jasmine ran into trouble in the marketplace. Jasmine saw a poor little boy who looked hungry, so she handed him an apple.

"I don't have any money," stammered Jasmine to the fruit seller who demanded payment.

Aladdin rushed to help. "Follow me!" he cried, leading her through the alleys of Agrabah.

After outrunning the guards, Jasmine and Aladdin got to know each other better. They discovered that they had a lot in common. Jasmine felt trapped and longed for a change. Aladdin felt exactly the same way! He also wanted a change. He didn't want to live on the streets anymore.

But suddenly, the palace guards rushed in and seized Aladdin!

"Let him go by order of the Princess!" cried Jasmine, revealing her true identity as the princess.

"We have orders from Jafar," said the guard.

Jafar was the Sultan's chief adviser, and he was an evil man.

Jafar had been watching Aladdin a long time. Jafar needed a Diamond in the Rough to enter a magical cave, the Cave of Wonders. Inside the Cave of Wonders was a magic lamp, and Jafar believed that Aladdin could find it for him.

And Jafar had plans for Jasmine, too! When got hold of the magic lamp, he could have anything he wanted, and he wanted to marry Jasmine.

Jafar disguised himself as an old prisoner.
"I need a man to find the lamp that is hidden in
the Cave of Wonders," Jafar told Aladdin. "If you
find it, you will be rewarded with treasures."

Aladdin wanted to be rich, so he agreed to help.

Jafar, Aladdin, and Abu soon arrived at the
Cave. "Who disturbs my slumber?" the Cave roared.

"It is I," Aladdin said.

"Touch nothing but the lamp," the Cave warned.

Aladdin entered the Cave. He walked down
hundreds of winding steps and saw piles of gold.
Suddenly a carpet started to move. It was a Magic
Carpet. It led Aladdin right to the magic lamp. But
while Aladdin was getting the lamp, Abu saw a
shiny ruby. He reached out to take it.

"You have touched the forbidden treasure!" the Cave bellowed as it started to crumble.

All around them gold exploded and started to melt. It popped and bubbled like hot lava.

Aladdin made it to the mouth of the Cave just in time. He reached for Jafar's hand.

"Give me the lamp first," Jafar ordered.

Aladdin handed it to him. But Jafar did not help him out of the Cave. Instead, he pushed Aladdin back in. Abu jumped in after Aladdin, but not before Abu grabbed the lamp away from Jafar.

When Aladdin rubbed the dusty lamp, out sprang a giant blue genie! "I'm the Genie of the Lamp!" he cried. "You set me free, so you get three wishes. And no wishing for more wishes."

"Wish?" Aladdin asked. "I only wish that I were a wealthy prince so I could marry Jasmine."

"Then I'll make you a prince!" said the Genie. Suddenly, Aladdin was dressed in fine clothes.

Aladdin presented himself to Jasmine as a prince, but Jafar had another evil plan. He stole the magic lamp from Aladdin, who had used his second wish to get away from Jafar. Aladdin tricked Jafar into wishing to become a powerful genie. With the wish, Jafar was sucked into the lamp and gone forever!

But Aladdin was sad. He had lied to Jasmine. Jasmine was very special to him, but Aladdin could not pretend he was something he was not. He wasn't a prince, so he couldn't marry her. Besides, he wanted to use his last wish to free the Genie.

"I would do just about anything to be with you, Jasmine," Aladdin said. "But I cannot lie to you. I'm not a prince. I'm not rich. In fact, I have nothing."

The Sultan was so impressed with Aladdin's honesty, he decided to change the law so that Jasmine could marry whomever she wished.

"I wish to marry Aladdin!" said Jasmine.

And *that* wish didn't require a genie!

Jasmine: A Story of Honesty

Honesty means telling the truth. Sometimes we are afraid to tell the truth because we might get in trouble, or because lying seems easier.

It wasn't easy for Aladdin to tell the truth, but it was important. Aladdin could have pretended to be a prince, but he cared too much about Jasmine to lie to her. More than treasure, Aladdin wanted to be honest and true to himself.

And more than anything, Jasmine wanted to be true to her heart. That's why Aladdin and Jasmine's love was worth more than gold!